DITCHMEN

Woken by the Hoedag

"Enjoy the Struggle"

JOE GINTER

ISBN 979-8-89112-373-1 (Paperback)
ISBN 979-8-89112-374-8 (Digital)

Covenant Books
11661 Hwy 707
Murrells Inlet, SC 29576
www.covenantbooks.com

ACKNOWLEDGMENTS

Just before I retired at the end of the 2022–2023 school year, I had my final students advise me on my plans for *Ditchmen 4*. One suggestion they had was to have more of what they called humor doodles. These are the rough sketches that enhance some of the more humorous parts of the story. I would like to thank all my former students for inspiring me to continue chasing my dream of having a screenplay made into a movie, and to remind them that "old teachers don't fade away, they just sit in the hallway and eat bologna sandwiches."

As suggested, once again a terminology key:

- Fade in: a process in which the picture is from a darkened screen to a fully lighted screen.
- Fade out: the same process as above but in reverse.
- Cut to: an editing technique that generally is avoided and left normally to the director to determine abrupt camera transitions. It is used in this book to help the reader with what they visualize next.
- Dissolve to: used as a time lapse, not to be confused with cutting from shot to shot.
- Series of shots: literally a series of shots run one after another.
- Close up: a shot that emphasizes a detail, for example, a ball or a sign.
- Close shot: shows a character from the shoulders up.
- POV shot: Abbreviation for point of view. It is a cinematic trick used to present a scene, so the audience sees it through the eyes of a particular character.

- Pan shot: a horizontal camera movement in which the camera pivots left or right while its base remains in fixed location.

FADE IN

OFF SCREEN the opening song begins, "Somebody Slap Me" by John Anderson. Superimposed on the screen is Ditchmen 4: Woken by the Hoedag, *as well as opening credits.*

SERIES OF SHOTS of people of the St. Marys, Ohio, area enjoying Grand Lake St. Marys right before the Fourth of July holiday weekend. Fishing, boating, camping, swimming, picnicking is shown. "Warning: Algae Bloom—Do not Swim" signs are shown being yanked out of the ground.

It's been eight months since Halloween when lightning struck teacher/scientist Amy Griner's concoction, which had landed earlier on the local high school's turf field, creating "Turfie." It was Turfie who was instrumental in saving the city of St. Marys from the treacherous "Dirt Cake," a failed version to duplicate the Ditchmen by defense contractor Stan Bando.

Fifteen months before, twelve developmentally improved Ditchmen and the townspeople joined together to prevent outside forces from stealing Amy's research. These outside forces included Stan Bando, Dianne Green from the EPA, investigative reporter Richard Carty, and Bert Campy representing Silicon Valley. Supporting them or doing their dirty work was their Special Covert Unit Managers, SCUM.

Ten months earlier than that, hundreds of Ditchmen inadvertently attack the city of St. Marys, only to be stopped by language arts teacher/spouse Jay Griner and the townspeople. This is also when the unorthodox Jay discovered that his not-late wife was still alive and responsible for the Ditchmen phenomenon.

1

Opening song ends

    The camera zooms from an AERIAL SHOT of the lake to a speed-boat containing Clay and Debbie along with another couple. The young, sometimes unassured Clay is still Amy Griner's lone lab assistant. The opportunistic Debbie jumped at the chance to purchase the Have a Fit, Stay Fit Health Center once Vance Wringer, Stan Bando's stooge, proved to be a conspirator against the Griners. The other couple is her new business partner, Jolie, and her boyfriend, Tucker.

DEBBIE. What a beautiful day! Thanks so much for inviting us.
JOLIE. We are more than business partners. We've been working so
    hard since we bought Have a Fit, Stay Fit. We hadn't had any
    time to have any fun together. One of us is always managing
    the fitness center. Besides, Tucker has been dying to bring his
    boat up to this lake.
TUCKER. Tell me about this lake.

DEBBIE. Clay's the expert on that.
CLAY. Well, it was manmade. A thousand and seven hundred men,
    mostly Irish and German immigrants working for 30 cents a
    day, started digging it in 1837 and finished in 1845. Its seven-
    teen thousand acres and was used to supply water for the Miami
    and Erie Canals. The railroad ended the canal era.
DEBBIE. You see? What did I tell you?
TUCKER. Love this stuff. What about the two cities on each side?

CLAY. Well, of course you got St. Marys on the east, and Celina on the west. Both are filled with people who love to enjoy life. They are rivals in high school sports. The lake's name is a touchy issue for some. Both towns have had an Ohio State legend as a native. Galen Cisco for St. Marys and Jim Otis for Celina. And even though St. Marys has gotten a lot of notoriety recently due to the Ditchmen, both get to claim the Hoedag.

TUCKER. "Hoedag"? What's a Hoedag?

JOLIE. I've never even heard of the Hoedag.

CLAY. Well, you must remember it's Hoedag, H-O-E. not H-O. That Hodag is a Wisconsin folklore critter that is bull-horned with a row of thick curved spines down its back and was part of the Paul Bunyan stories. This lake's Hoedag first appeared in 1912 just as the oil boom ended.

TUCKER. "Oil boom"?

CLAY. Yes, back in 1886, oil was first discovered in St. Marys, in what is today Armstrong Park. But the bulk of the oil and natural gas was drilled from the lake here. Oil derricks covered this area until around 1910.

TUCKER. Now about this Hoedag. Tell me more, tell me more.

DEBBIE (interrupting). Let's sing him the Hoedag song that Jay made up.

CLAY. Sure, if they don't mind.

TUCKER. I got to hear it.

JOLIE. Especially now.

CLAY. It happens to be the best way to describe it.

CLAY, DEBBIE, (singing to the tune of Mitch Miller's "Must Be
    Santa") Who's got a neck like a giraffe?
    Hoedag has neck like a giraffe
    Whose head is that of a horse?
    Hoedag's head is that of a horse
    Neck like a giraffe
    Head of a horse
    Must be Hoedag, must be Hoedag
    Must be the Hoe-oe-dag
    Who's got a body like a dragon?
    Hoedag's got a body like a dragon
    Who's got the tail with a red eyeball?
    Hoedag's got a tail with a red eyeball
    Red eyeball tail
    Dragon body
    Head of a horse
    Neck like a giraffe
    Must be Hoedag, must be Hoedag
    Must be the Hoe-oe-dag
    Who's got teeth like a gator?
    Hoedag has teeth like a gator
    Who's got a green third eye?
    Hoedag's got a third green eye?
    Third green eye
    Gator teeth
    Red eyeball tail
    Dragon body
    Head of a horse
    Neck like a giraffe
    Must be Hoedag, must be Hoedag
    Must be the Hoe-oe-dag
    Who's got feet like a chicken?

4

Hoedag's got feet like a chicken
Who's got a hump that's like a backward fin?
Hoedag's got a hump like a backward fin
Backward fin
Chicken feet
Third green eye
Gator teeth
Red eyeball tail
Dragon Body
Head of a horse
Neck like a giraffe
Must be Hoedag, must be Hoedag
Must be the Hoe-oe-dag!

Tucker and Jolie applaud and cheer their effort.

TUCKER. I just got to see this thing.
JOLIE. Remember, Tucker, we're here to ski.
TUCKER. You're right. Clay, you are up first.
CLAY. You bet.
DEBBIE. Wow, I'm impressed. I didn't even know you ski.
CLAY. What can I say?

Clay, with Jolie's help, prepares to ski as Tucker steers the boat.

JOLIE. Debbie, you need to sit here and keep an eye on Clay. I will
    be up by Tucker.

*Tucker takes off and pulls Clay right up. Clay, not exactly looking
like a pro, starts to shout out at Debbie.*

CLAY. Debbie, our romance started with a water fight against the
    Ditchmen! And ever since then, you have made me feel like I'm
    walking on water! So I thought it is only natural that I propose
    to you while I'm skiing. Debbie, will you marry me?

Clay pulls out an engagement ring box from his swimsuit and holds it toward her.

DEBBIE. Oh my gosh, oh my gosh!

Suddenly before she could give him an answer, the large, very hard hump of the Hoedag pops right out of the water. It is in the reverse shape of a shark's fin, so it served as a perfect ramp for Clay as he is launched clear over the boat. The engagement ring case is launched out of his hand as well. Tucker slows the boat as he catches up to Clay.

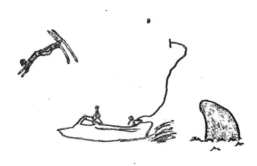

DEBBIE. Clay, are you all, right? My ring, my ring!

CLAY. Did you see that? What do you mean by "my ring"? Does that mean you say yes?

Clay starts to get into the boat. Debbie hugs and kisses him.

TUCKER. That had to be the Hoedag.
JOLIE. The hump was exactly like the way you described it in the song.
DEBBIE. I don't care about my ring as long as you're all right.

Clay reaches into one of the boat's compartments on its dashboard and pulls out the engagement ring as Debbie screams with joy.

CLAY. I was too worried to keep the ring in the box.
DEBBIE. That's my Clay.

They hug and celebrate, forgetting for now the terror that they just experienced.

DISSOLVE TO

A few days later, Winnie's Cryptid Crusade *reality show tour bus driving down the highway a few miles from St. Marys. It is followed by a semitruck filled with equipment and numerous vans filled with support staff. Winnie Washington, the diva of cryptologists, is often described as Oprah looking for Bigfoot. Winnie and her crew, led by the efficient and energetic executive producer Brandi, are preparing for their next episode. They will be looking for evidence and possibly even locate the Hoedag. Their caravan passes by some familiar sites like the Have a Fit, Stay Fit Health Center (which Debbie is now part owner), Amy's lab, and the nearby cemetery (which has been completely rehabilitated). All the bodies have been restored and returned to their proper plot after being launched out of their coffins and vaults eight months ago when Dirt Cake interfered with Amy's Ditchmen research.*

Brandi, with her clipboard, walks back to converse with Winnie, who is behind the door of her private quarters.

BRANDI. Our ETA is about ten to fifteen minutes. We'll be cranking your entrance song soon.

WINNIE. Oh good. How's the new driver?

BRANDI. I think he'll work out just fine.

WINNIE. That's a relief.

BRANDI. Did you have a chance to read your prep sheet?

WINNIE. Yes. Now I don't see anything about Neil Armstrong. I thought these lake towns fight over which is his hometown.

BRANDI. That would be Wapakoneta, eleven miles to the east of St. Marys. Celina is eleven miles to the west. NASA named Wapakoneta as his hometown when he lived longer in St. Marys during his childhood.

WINNIE. Why did they do that?

BRANDI. It's where his parents were living when he walked on the moon.

WINNIE. I see. On a more current event, St. Marys is the home of the Helmet Pizza, the latest pizza craze.

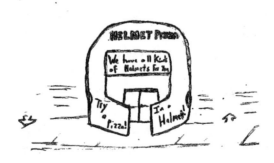

BRANDI. Yes, we'll be passing the original franchise soon.

WINNIE. I want to try their pizza in a helmet.

BRANDI. Duly noted.

WINNIE. Were you able to hire consultants for this episode?

BRANDI. Yes, a retired sheriff and a retired police chief. Both have investigated numerous Hoedag sightings. I also rented a newly renovated ballroom built in 1895 as our headquarters for the week.

WINNIE. Oh, that's exciting.

BRANDI. Did you like my amendments to the local history?

WINNIE. Yes, yes, I did. It should raise some eyebrows.

BRANDI. And get the media's attention. Controversy is free advertising. We need something more than that skier incident a few days ago.

WINNIE. But we don't want a frenzy.

BRANDI. Correct. Time for your song.

WINNIE. I am a little confused about all this "Ditchmen, Dirt Cake" stuff.

BRANDI. Let me explain. The Ditchmen is the creation of a local scientist-a woman, Amy Griner-nearly three years ago. It is basically dirt covered with grass, weeds, and litter. Her research got a little out of control and attacked the town. The townspeople averted the attack. But when the government sent a task force to steal her research ten months later, the Ditchmen and townspeople joined forces to foil their plans. Get this: the task force henchmen's acronym spelled SCUM. Finally, fifteen months ago, an individual from the task force tried to duplicate the research and created a less-friendly version called Dirt Cake. At the same time, Griner evolved these Ditchmen into a more developed product made from turf.

WINNIE. Wow, thanks for not putting all of that in your notes for me. Brandi, time for my song.

Brandi then walks up to the driver.

BRANDI. Time to crank her music.
DRIVER. "Wells Fargo Wagon" from the *Music Man* soundtrack beginning to play.
BRANDI. You want to know why "Wells Fargo Wagon"?
DRIVER. Not necessary, I just drive.
BRANDI. It was her mother's favorite song from her favorite musical. It's her tradition as we reach our destination to enter with that tune.

Brandi turns and walks away.

DRIVER. (To himself) The Music Man was a scammer.

OFF SCREEN the "Wells Fargo Wagon" song from the Music Man *soundtrack begins to play.*

CUT TO

SERIES OF SHOTS of Winnie's caravan of vehicles arriving in town. This includes the Helmet Pizza establishment, the brainchild of one-time pizza delivery boy Stevie, who has become a successful entrepreneur practically overnight.

An incredible crowd of fans stand near the curb. The closer to the mayor's office, the denser the crowd.

CUT TO

Mayor Ted and wife Leslie Greer-Horn, the prim and proper Camelot couple of St. Marys, as they appear to form a welcome committee as the song ends.

The tour bus comes to a stop, and only Brandi exits. Winnie's make-up artist and hair stylist enter.

TED HORN. Welcome to St. Marys. I am Mayor Horn, and this is my wife, Leslie Greer-Horn.
BRANDI. I am obviously not Winnie. We'll be here an hour before she is ready to join us. She likes only her most loyal fans to see her. I am Brandi, the executive producer for Winnie's *Cryptid Crusade*. We can go on in and get started with our meeting.

They enter the building as the crowd continues with their frenzy.

CUT TO

A conference room filling up with city officials, media, and some more of Winnie's support staff.

TED. I'm glad to have you here. I only wish we had more time to prepare for you. You see, Amy Griner and Turfie are in Columbus appearing on a talk show. They are not expected to be back until tomorrow.

LESLIE. We would love to treat you all to dinner tonight.

TED. *(hesitating)* We would? *(Pause as Leslie gives him a look of insistence)* We would!

BRANDI. I'm afraid there appears to be a misunderstanding. We are not here to film an episode about the Ditchmen.

WINNIE, dressed immaculately like a flamboyant CEO, enters and steals the conversation.

WINNIE. We are not here to seek an audience with…Turfie, is it?

She looks at Brandi, and she nods.

WINNIE. It's man-made, or in this case woman-made. That's not our cup of tea. We are here to discover the Hoedag.

Ted and Leslie look at each other.

TED. The Hoedag?

WINNIE. A few days ago, a local skier experienced a terrifying encounter.

TED. I'm aware of the incident.

LESLIE. That skier is a friend of ours.

TED. I haven't had the opportunity to speak with him yet.

BRANDI. By the way, this is Winnie Washington of Winnie's *Cryptid Crusade* Reality Show. Winnie, this is Mayor—

WINNIE. Ted Horn and his lovely wife, Mrs. Green-Horn.

LESLIE. Greer-Horn.

WINNIE. I'm so sorry, my mistake. Now the first recorded sighting of this cryptid was back in 1912. Shortly after the lake's oil and natural gas boom fizzled due to the bigger oil boom in Texas. Most likely this cryptid emerged from one of the abandoned natural gas cavities. Cryptids, for those of you who don't watch my show, are what you call creatures that haven't been proven to exist. Then in the early 1930s, it destroyed your Gordon State Park. You know the amusement park, the Devil's Backbone rollercoaster, the pavilion that hosted such performers as Sammy Kay and Guy Lombardo.

TED. I always thought a tornado and two fires destroyed Gordon State Park?

WINNIE. You see, you've got to think like a cryptid. Do you really think it wanted an attraction to exist that brought thousands to the lake? And in 1986, that wasn't an earthquake that this area experienced.

LESLIE. I remember that earthquake. It took place at four in the morning.

WINNIE. Four twenty-three to be exact. A 4.2 on the Richter scale. I'd say the Hoedag was sure angry that night. So to wrap things up for this initial meeting, we hired two local consultants.

Brandi points to them Al and Tim, who had entered late. They wave at Ted and Leslie.

TED. We know them.

LESLIE. Also our friends.

TED. Coming out of retirement?

AL. What can we say?

TIM. We're just looking to be relevant again.

WINNIE. The world is addicted to relevancy. Now we rented your ballroom above your beautiful Grand Theater. The theater, which was built in 1895 and in 1910, was part of that clever stunt in which people thought an elephant was tightrope walking across the top of the theater and the building across the street. Of course, it was two men in an elephant costume.

LESLIE. I'm impressed with your knowledge of our community.

WINNIE. I remember the important things, dear. We start searching for the Hoedag tomorrow. Thank you for your hospitality.

Winnie turns and exits, whispering to Brandi on her way out.

WINNIE. Are you proud of me?

BRANDI. You studied my notes.

CUT TO

TED. Wow, she's something.

LESLIE. I don't trust her.

DISSOLVE TO

SERIES OF SHOTS of downtown Columbus, Ohio, as OFF SCREEN "Money Honey" by the Bay City Rollers begins to play.

CUT TO

Inside a Columbus television studio with a live audience as a segment of an enthusiastically hosted talk show featuring Amy Griner and Turfie resumes from a commercial break. OFF SCREEN the song ends.

BOBBY. Welcome back to *Columbus AM* with Ruthie and of course me, Bobby. We are continuing our conversation with teacher-scientist Amy Griner and her creation, her pet, her Frankenstein. What do you call Turfie?

AMY. My friend.

RUTHIE. Is he considered AI?

TURFIE. No, I'm AT.

RUTHIE. "AT"?

TURFIE. Artificial turf.

Bobby and Ruthie both cackle.

RUTHIE. Why aren't you considered artificial intelligence?

AMY. Turfie currently is not marketable as AI, so there's no opportunity for anyone to make a buck. Therefore, Turfie is dismissed by the science community. Unfortunately, science is becoming more about making money not discoveries.

BOBBY. Now before the commercial break you were explaining how your first batch of Ditchmen were created. You discovered that some kind of by-product was emitting from the windmills in your area into the soil. Then this was mixed with agricultural runoff in the ditches. That part is very much like how the algae bloom is formulated in many of our water sources. Just too much phosphorus and nitrogen.

AMY. Correct.

BOBBY. Now the part I am having trouble comprehending is what happens in rural cemeteries. This is the part that makes it sound like Frankenstein. You say remnants of the souls from the graves mixes with substance from the ditches, and voila, you have a Ditchman.

AMY. It is more like the residue of the remnants of the souls. It doesn't include any aspect of the person that was once alive.

BOBBY. Then you need a bolt of lightning or some big laboratory equipment to harness it.

AMY. Not necessarily. Just a little jolt could do it, but not always.

TURFIE. You know, the same laboratory equipment used in the original *Frankenstein* movie was also used in *Young Frankenstein*.

RUTHIE. Is that right?

AMY. Turfie has become a sponge for pop culture trivia.

RUTHIE. So you are not AI. You know you are no Marvel character with superpowers. You are not an alien from a different planet. So you're not ET?

TURFIE. No I'm AT. *(Pause as audience chuckles)* My ancestors were described as a combination of Gumby and Bigfoot. I'm more like just Gumby.

RUTHIE. Your ancestors? Those Ditchmen were around only three years ago. How can they be your ancestors?

TURFIE. My family tree is more of a shrub than a tree.

BOBBY. Turfie, do you have a job?

TURFIE. I am a professional lid opener.

AMY. He does have incredible strength and is often called on to open jars and containers for the elderly around town. He is involved in numerous charitable activities in the community including a safe Fourth of July celebration for local youth.

RUTHIE. I see. Well, being green, do you see yourself as a person of color?

TURFIE. I am turf. I don't know why everyone is so hung up on skin color. There's no skin in heaven.

AMY. He is a fan of movies. Lately he has been watching the 1970s *Billy Jack* films. I had to quickly teach him about turning the other cheek, not to wallop others in the face with your feet.

BOBBY. I understand this is your first visit to a big city. What are
your impressions of it?

TURFIE. Too much crime. What's with these gangs? Young people
need to get together and play whiffie ball—not Wiffle—or red
rover. Not get together and be mean and cause trouble. This
town is getting to be like the movie *The Warriors*. I heard there's
a gang that wears hoodies and vintage Archie masks. They call
themselves the Archies—you know the comic book character.
Weird. They easily could be called the Howdy Doodys or the
Opie Taylors. Another gang called the Roadkill Crew wear flo-
rescent vests and red paint on their face. They look like state
workers. Maybe they fight one person at a time, and the others
stand around and watch. Is there a head guy like in *The Warriors*
movie that reaches his arms out and shouts, "Can you dig it!"

*Turfie finishes his imitation, and the studio audience cheers him
wildly.*

RUTHIE. Well, this sure has been fun. And for joining us
today, we have a very special gift. We want you to help us make our
earth a less-polluted place, so we got you the most luxurious bidet on
the market!

Audience applauses

AMY. Wow a bidet. My husband, Jay, is going to love that.
BOBBY. I love mine!
AMY. Well, he has worn an ostomy bag since 1984.
TURFIE. He's closed for business in the back, and I'm turf.
AMY. I'm sure he'll figure something out. He's back home with our
    son Reggie and our grandson Hack, who has a ballgame today.
TURFIE. Reggie moved back to be my business manager.

Turfie gives the audience another "Can you dig it!" to the chagrin of Bobby and Ruthie.

DISSOLVE TO

SERIES OF SHOTS of a ballpark where youth are having a game. OFF SCREEN "Shy Boy" by Bananarama begins to play. You have shots of players doing good and players doing bad. You have shots of parents being glad and parents being mad. Song ends.

CUT TO

Jay Griner sitting in a lawn chair with his son Reggie on the first base side of the ball diamond. They are cheering on Reggie's son Hack. Reggie is Jay and Amy's adopted son. He has overcome the autism spectrum to be a successful nonprofit manager and to have his own family. Reggie and his wife, who is a lawyer, have been out west for some time. They decided Reggie would move back with their son Hack to manage Turfie's business and charitable affairs. She will join them once she completes her commitments. In the meantime, Reggie has added Stevie as a client in his business venture.

REGGIE. Have you heard from Mom yet?
JAY. Yes. They're done. She said they were given a gift of a bidet for
    their appearance.
REGGIE. A bidet! That's funny.

JAY. Yeah, it's hysterical. It's what I always wanted since 1984.

REGGIE. I guess you'll just have to enjoy the struggle with that.

JAY. Very funny. Watching this game is making me nervous.

REGGIE. Bringing back memories of watching me?

JAY. You have no idea. Hack is a heck of a player.

REGGIE. And I was a nightmare.

JAY. That wasn't your fault. We adopted you when you were three months. You were incredibly athletic. I should know since I was once a track coach. We had no idea of the prenatal neglect and that not being held and hardly fed those first three months would have such an effect on you developmentally. Your hand-and-eye coordination was delayed. You didn't understand the concept of competing.

REGGIE. You practiced with me every day.

JAY. And I looked like the father that spent no time with their kid. I think it was God's way of keeping me humble. If you were a star, I'd have been the embarrassing parent. Probably would have even gotten a tattoo of your name on my arm. Maybe even create a candy bar after you.

REGGIE. A candy bar? That was already done with another Reggie. You raised me right. Despite my disabilities, you kept your expectations of me high.

JAY. When it comes to teaching students with special needs, you have got to be Sheriff Andy and believe it or not. Sometimes you've got to Deputy Barney Fife. Look at you now, Mr. Successful Business Manager.

REGGIE. Was I really that bad? (chuckling)

JAY. Every time you got to third base, you would never go to home plate. You always next headed right for the dugout.

REGGIE. Maybe baseball wasn't my sport.

JAY. Then what was your sport? Soccer? You once did get two goals in under ten seconds. One for each team. How about basketball? A referee once handed you the ball to throw in bounds, and you instead drove to the hoop. The referee brought you back, handed you the ball again after explaining what to do. And once again you drove to the hoop. Also, one basketball game, you were on offense, and the opposing coach hollered at the top of his lungs "Put your hands up!" Out of the ten players on the court, you were the only one that put their hands up. Then there's football. You stood in your stance every play until you heard the whistle blow ending each play. That resulted in you late hitting someone play after play.

REGGIE. Now I had to improve as I got older, especially with all your creative workouts like the DPBT, the decline plank, backward treadmill.

JAY. Let's see—in track, you broke the stagger in the two-hundred-meter dash by the second curve, only to coast the rest of the way. When asked about that afterward, you said that you didn't want to pass your friend.

REGGIE. You always remained patient with me. You never got ridiculous.

JAY. Like that father.

Jay and Reggie get up when they begin to witness a father losing his temper with his son after getting picked off first base to end the game. They walk up to the fence line.

JAY. Come on, Louis, everyone makes mistakes. In fact, I believe you still owe me detentions for some of yours.

LOUIS. Mr. G., he knows better.

JAY. What did I always tell you?

LOUIS. You know I still remember. You said, "When in hot water, be like a tea bag and rise to the top."

Jay raises his hands as if to say, "There you are." Louis then begins to encourage his son. Reggie and Jay return to their lawn chairs. Hack joins them.

REGGIE. Great game, Hack.

HACK. Thanks, and thank you, Grandpa, for helping Rollie. He didn't mean to get picked off. Does his dad really owe you detentions?

JAY. Naw, when you retire, all detentions are wiped out. And your dad's right, you played great. Although you did have a farmer bunt.

HACK. I did? What's a farmer bunt?

JAY. When your coach gives you the bunt signal, and you hit it over the fence. You know, because farm kids are usually very strong.

HACK. Oh. But I didn't have a farmer bunt. That was last week's bunt signal.

JAY. You change your signals? Not a bad idea.

HACK. Can we get pop and popcorn from the concession stand and
  stay for a few innings of the next game?
REGGIE. If it is all right with Grandpa.
JAY. Sure, I will even pay for the pop and popcorn.
HACK. Can you go get it? I don't want to wait in that really long
  line.
JAY. I don't want to go get it either.
REGGIE. Me neither.
JAY. I'll tell you what. We'll have a coin-flip tournament. And you
  can even have a bye.
HACK. Cool, I get a bye.

Jay takes out a quarter and prepares to flip it.

JAY. Call it, son.
REGGIE. Tails.

Jay removes his hand, revealing that the coin is indeed tails.

JAY. Looks like it's down to you and me, Hack. Call it.
HACK. Heads.

Jay flips it and removes his hand, revealing the coin is instead tails.

HACK. Darn.
JAY. It's tails. You go. Here's some money.

Hack starts toward the concession stand and then turns around.

HACK. Say, I thought byes were a good thing.
JAY. Not always.

*Hack continues on his way to the concession stand. Suddenly walking
by Jay is Murph, a harmless elderly man who seldom talked. A veteran of
the Korean War, Murph was never quite the same upon his return home.
He would remind you of a homeless Vic Morrow, the actor decapitated by*

a chopper blade back in 1980 on the set of the movie The Twilight Zone. *Murph walks by them and speaks without making eye contact.*

MURPH. You should have seen your father as a kid.

REGGIE. I see. Thanks for the info, Murph.

JAY. Thanks a lot. Murph and I always thought of you as my good luck charm. When I was coaching whenever he showed up, we won.

REGGIE. I probably know some of these stories like what you wrote in Mom's yearbook before you guys started dating. You meant to write "To the sweetest girl," but instead you wrote "To the sweatiest girl."

JAY. Very funny. I think Murph is talking about the time I was a bat-boy, and I had to go to the bathroom. Back then there were no restrooms in these parks, so my dad told me to go out the lone tree in center field. Well, I ran out there, and I went in front of the tree instead of behind like I was supposed to. There are a lot more stories you know.

REGGIE. I can't wait to hear them all again someday. Speaking of stories, I remember Grandpa telling me the story about once hiring Murph to paint the outside of the house.

JAY. And he tried to wallpaper the outside of the house instead.
REGGIE. That's it.
JAY. My dad didn't even get upset with him and still paid him.
REGGIE. That truly was love thy neighbor.

DISSOLVE TO

OFF SCREEN "Money Honey" by the Bay City Rollers resumes playing. Amy and Turfie enter a parking garage. It is now dusk. They are soon surrounded by a half-dozen members of the Archies, with dark hoodies and vintage Archie masks. Backing them up are some members of the Roadkill Crew, with fluorescent safety vests and red-painted faces. OFF SCREEN the song ends.

TURFIE. Say, fellas, never would have guessed that you would be daytime TV watchers. I look at some of you, and I want to start singing, "Sugar, oh honey, honey. You are my candy girl, and you got me wanting you."
ONE OF THE ARCHIES. Red rover, red rover. Let Turfie come over.

Turfie then leans down near Amy's ear.

TURFIE. I'm just going to give them one wallop, then turn the other cheek, pick you up, and skedaddle out of here.
AMY. Why not just skedaddle?
TURFIE. Okay, gentlemen, make my early evening!

Turfie moves in a little closer and swings his long right leg from his seven-foot frame, wiping out all six members of the Archie gang like a row of dominoes. The Roadkill Crew gang immediately charge. Turfie, with one arm, picks up Amy like a football and mounts a retreat. He runs out of the parking garage and down the street. He soon approaches a fire hydrant and reaches out with one hand, unscrewing the side and top of the hydrant without hardly breaking stride. Water gushes out of the hydrant just as the gang members reach it. Some fall, others merely lose their balance briefly. Turfie and Amy are pretty much out of sight.

DISSOLVE TO

A wooden area right offshore from the lake at dusk. OFF SCREEN "The Zoo" by the Scorpions begin to play. Retired sheriff Al and retired police chief Tim are busy setting up trail cameras all around the lake. The song pauses.

AL. I thought being a consultant meant you don't have to do anything.
TIM. Me too. This is worse than a stakeout.

They walk over to the next spot for a trail camera.

TIM. You know, I said something like, retiring was losing that feeling of being relevant.
AL. Yes, something like that back at that meeting.
TIM. That was stupid of me.

Suddenly they hear some branches cracking nearby. They both freeze and give a look to each other.

AL. That was silly of us.

CLOSE SHOT of the Hoedag's chicken feet plucking a trail camera off a tree.

AL. I think we have done enough consulting for one night.
TIM. I agree.

CUT TO

The Hoedag growling and making his presence known by showing off his mouthful of trail cams. OFF SCREEN the song, "The Zoo" by the Scorpions resumes at the instrumental interlude portion. Al and Tim scream and take off running for their lives.

DISSOLVE TO

The morning of July 2 in the Grand Ballroom, which is now set up as Winnie's headquarters. It is arranged with lots of tables and chairs. On the tables are several laptops and film equipment. Of course, there is also a table set up with refreshments. Winnie is already there drilling one of her crew to find the trail camera feeds on his laptop.

WINNIE. Come on, they set up those trail cams last night. You should be getting a video feed.

WINNIE. Brandi!

BRANDI. Yes, Winnie, good morning.

WINNIE. Good morning. I thought you said those consultants you hired were reliable.

BRANDI. Absolutely reliable.

WINNIE. We're not getting any feeds. Do you know if they actually put trail cams up?

Retired sheriff Al and retired police chief Tim enter with a definite purpose.

Al. We did, and that thing out there was taking them down as fast as we put them up.

BRANDI. What thing?

AL. The Hoedag.

WINNIE. The Hoedag?

TIM. We were hired as consultants, not bait.

BRANDI. You saw it?

TIM. As close as you are to me.

WINNIE. They saw it.

AL. It looked like something that could breathe fire.

WINNIE. Excuse me gentlemen, I need to meet alone with my staff.
    I promise, nothing but consulting here on out.

BRANDI. Yes, she promises.

*They are grateful. Brandi sees them to the exit. Winnie's staff then
all gather around her.*

WINNIE. Everybody, listen up. We might have an actual cryptid
    here.

CREW MEMBER. We have never had an actual cryptid before.

BRANDI. Do you guys know what that means?

WINNIE. We will have to film what really happens, not just the
    evidentials.

BRANDI. No staging things, no creating suspense. We need to
    spend the entire night and be on our toes.

ANOTHER CREW MEMBER. So we'll be a genuine reality show
    tonight.

The crew cheers.

WINNIE. That means I need to take a nap. But first, Brandi, you
    promised to take me to Helmet Pizza for lunch.

BRANDI. All right, everybody, double check your equipment. Make
    sure you are prepared. We'll start filming at dusk.

DISSOLVE TO

LONG SHOT of the Griner Farm.

CUT TO

　　Inside Griner Farm, breakfast is being prepared. Jay, Amy, and Turfie are all pitching in. Amy is at the stove, Jay setting the table, and Turfie is at the toaster, adding to its tower of already-made toast. Reggie and Hack are also arriving at the breakfast area. Reggie's wife is still out west, wrapping up business before she joins them.

HACK. I just got done FaceTiming my mom. She's almost done with her business things out west, so she can join us soon.

REGGIE. Isn't that great? She told me last night.

AMY. I'm so proud of you, Hack. You have been so courageous to help your dad move back to Ohio and be away from your mom until she is able to transfer.

JAY. Is that a dig at me?

AMY. No. Why would you think such a thing?

JAY. He knows his mom is alive. Remember, I thought you were six feet under.

AMY. You were very courageous too, dear.

REGGIE. Maybe you were being humbled again.

JAY. Very funny. Enjoy the struggle everyone. You always got to keep enjoying the struggle. *(Pause as he notices Turfie's tower of toast.)* Turfie, that might be enough toast for this morning.

TURFIE. You never know when you might buy a round of toast.

JAY. There's another dig. This isn't the diner downtown.

TURFIE. You know, Hack, your dad becoming my business manager has been a godsend.

HACK. And for Stevie too.

AMY. There wouldn't be a Helmet Pizza if it weren't for your dad helping Stevie.

REGGIE. Let's keep in mind we have Ted's campfire outing tonight at the campgrounds. And tomorrow morning is the final meeting for Turfie's Safe and Crazy Fourth of the July Celebration for Youths. Looks like we have perfect weather all weekend.

JAY. You sure do sound like a business manager. Doesn't he, dear?

AMY. Sure does. You should have had him plan my funeral.

Jay smiles and throws a piece of toast at her.

AMY. By the way, do you have our new bidet installed yet?

DISSOLVE TO

SERIES OF SHOTS of Coach conducting summer training conditioning with his football players on one of the beaches located on Grand Lake St. Marys. OFF SCREEN the song "Last Child" by Aerosmith begins to play.

Coach blows his whistle to let his players have a moment of rest before the next sprint in the sand. Song pauses.

COACH. Don't forget, we have a need for speed! Feel your feet digging in the sand with every step. That will result in more explosions on the field.

He blows the whistle and resumes the conditioning. Song resumes.

After a few more sprints. He blows his whistle again for them to stop. This time he is disappointed in their effort. Song ends.

COACH. My grandma can move faster than most of you, and she died last spring.

CUT TO

A couple of assistant coaches standing off to one side. One assistant leans over to the other to make a comment.

ASSISTANT COACH. Like we haven't heard that story before.

CUT TO

Coach waving his players to come to him.

COACH. I need to see more hunger out here. Most of you had Mr. Griner before he retired. Well, he used to tell people the story about competing in the Punt, Pass, and Kick Competition. He was determined to win, and he ended up being the first and only person in the competition's history to have a negative total score. But that experience made him work a hundred times harder to improve. Ohio State Legend Coach Woody Hayes use to say about other coaches, "They might outsmart me, or be luckier, but they can't outwork me."

The players laugh.

CUT TO.

The two assistants again.

ASSISTANT COACH. That's just great. He's using the guy that beat us all up using pom-poms a couple of years ago as motivation.
OTHER ASSISTANT. Have you noticed Coach sort of changing?
ASSISTANT COACH. I know what you mean. He used to completely pattern himself after local legend Coach Cap.

CUT TO

PLAYER. How do you get a negative score in Punt, Pass, and Kick?

COACH. In Mr. Griner's defense, it was a rainy day. He fell on his kick. His punt went backward, and his pass slipped out of the back of his hand. Monday, we go to Ugh Hill for some backward running up it. Oh, I almost forgot, bring a medicine ball if you have one. Just a little variation that Mr. Griner showed me. ALL right, fun time. You have got twenty minutes before the bus heads back to the school.

The players immediately run into the lake.

PLAYER. Let's get the inner tubes and play king of the hill on the inflatable trampolines!

CUT TO

ASSISTANT COACH. I tell you, something is going on with Coach. Where's the clichés? Where's the potato chips?
OTHER ASSISTANT. I just don't know.

CUT TO

Outside the nearby marina, which is serving as the headquarters for the Crappiethon that's in progress. The goal in this fishing competition is to catch crappies that have been tagged for certain prizes donated by local businesses. Several contest officials around several tables are waiting for the fishermen to return with their catch. One official grab his binoculars and looks out onto the lake.

OFFICIAL. The weather couldn't be more perfect.

CUT TO

SERIES OF SHOTS of fishermen fishing on their boats out on their lake. OFF SCREEN the interlude to "The Zoo" begins to play once again.

Suddenly, one at a time, fishermen are yanked by their fishing lines right out of their boats.

CUT TO

The Crappiethon official that was using his binoculars.

OFFICIAL. Holy Hoedag!

CUT TO

The football players four at time wearing inner tubes on two differ-ent trampolines playing king of the hill.

CUT TO

The large hump of the Hoedag that resembles a reverse shark fin emerging out of the water heading right for the trampolines as the song continues. It isn't long before it draws near and submerges.

CUT TO

SERIES OF SHOTS of the hump blasting the two tramps from underneath and launching the players still in their inner tubes way up into the air. Some are as high as a four-story building. You hear the screams of agony of the players as they land on the water like human bobbers, jolting their armpit joints. Cries of "My pits, oh my arm pits," echo along the beach area.

DISSOLVE TO

The Helmet Pizza, where the latest craze in pizza is off to a busy lunch time. OFF SCREEN "Promises" by Eric Clapton begins to play.

CUT TO

CLOSE UP of Stevie's motorcycle helmet carefully displayed above the main counter.

SERIES OF SHOTS of the Helmet Pizza restaurant as the song, "Promises" by Eric Clapton continues to play.

After the CLOSE UP, the camera PANS down to a shot of the owner Stevie, without a helmet on. Other things shown in the SERIES of SHOTS are the different kinds of helmets available—football, baseball, and motorcycle. A pizza being made in a helmet is shown with its chunks of crust, thick sauce, lots of mozzarella cheese, and choice of various meats and toppings. Winnie and Brandi enter with Winnie receiving her usual celebrity reception. The song ends.

WINNIE. This place is wonderful. My, my, what do I order?
BRANDI. Very different.

Turfie then enters, greeted with an even bigger reception.

TURFIE. Why, you're Winnie Washington! What a pleasure to meet you! I just love your show!

Winnie stares in awe of the seven-footer.

WINNIE. The pleasure is all mine. Turfie?
TURFIE. That's right.
WINNIE. This is my executive producer, Brandi. Do you want to join us for lunch?
TURFIE. Thank you for asking, but I'll have to take a rain check. I'm just here to pick up a couple things from Stevie for my experiment.
WINNIE. Your experiment?
TURFIE. Good luck with your Hoedag searching.
WINNIE. Thank you. *(Pause as Turfie walks away)* Brandi, make a note of that. What could it be experimenting?

Turfie walks up and leans over the counter to greet Stevie with a hug and a handshake. Stevie reaches up, pulls his original helmet off the wall, and hands it to Turfie.

STEVIE. Take good care of it.

TURFIE. Sure thing. It's still odd not to see you wearing it. Now about the inflatable water bottle outside.

STEVIE. That you can keep.

TURFIE. Thanks, you're the best.

STEVIE. Anything for you, Turfie.

Turfie passes Winnie on his way out.

TURFIE. It was nice meeting you both. I hope we get the opportunity to meet again.

WINNIE. We got a rain check.

TURFIE. That's right, we do.

Turfie exits still be greeted like a celebrity.

WINNIE (to Brandi) It's so human-like.

BRANDI. Despite being seven foot and green.

CUT TO

Turfie walking out and beginning to take down the giant inflatable water bottle for his experiment.

CUT TO

Several television news crews' vehicles driving past the Pizza Helmet.

CUT TO

Winnie and Brandi at booth eating noticing the media vehicles driving by.

WINNIE. That's a lot of press arriving. This pizza in a helmet is delicious.

BRANDI. Wonder what's the hoopla is? You're right here.

A man in a nearby booth overhears and answers her.

MAN. The high school football team and crappie fishermen were attacked in the lake this morning.

WINNIE. Was anybody hurt?

MAN. From what I heard, just some strained shoulders.

BRANDI. Strained shoulders? That's odd.

WINNIE. Do you know what this means? Not only are we actually looking for something tonight. We may have competition. Let's go, I got to take my nap.

CUT TO

A Black Lincoln Town Car parked nearby. Two members of SCUM (Special Covert Unit Managers) slowly get out. They are dressed in casual beach wear. Gone are the dark suits and pants, and the flannel farm wear. They take a long, slow look-around and make their way to a lemonade stand being operated by a young boy and girl.

SCUM AGENT 1. We'll take a couple of lemonades.

YOUNG BOY. Right away, sir.

YOUNG GIRL. Say, you two look familiar. I remember you. You're SCUM.

SCUM AGENT. We are no longer Special Covert Unit Managers. We are now Special Corp Recovering Underwater Biological Species.

YOUNG GIRL. So, you're now SCRUBS. That's not much better.

YOUNG BOY. Are you after the Hoedag?

A third SCUM/SCRUBS agent sticks his head out of the nearby car.

SCRUBS AGENT 3. Hey, she wants you back in the car.

SCUM AGENT 1. *(After getting their drinks)* I guess I can't pay you. All I have is plastic.

YOUNG GIRL. No problem, we got a card machine. *(Showing them)*

They complete the transaction and get back into the car.

YOUNG BOY. Thanks, and have a good day, you SCRUBS.
YOUNG GIRL. I wonder who is in the backseat of that car.

DISSOLVE TO.
The Griner farm later that same afternoon. Turfie is walking about near the ditch. Hack walks out to see what he's doing.

HACK. Turfie, what are you doing?
TURFIE. Just doing some thinking. Why do you ask?
HACK. When I see a Ditchman by a ditch, I have to ask.
TURFIE. Technically, I'm turf.
HACK. That's just some side effect. It's almost time to leave for the
    camp out.
TURFIE. I'm afraid I'm not going.
HACK. Why not?
TURFIE. I need to go to the lab and do some last-minute planning
    for my Fourth of July Safe Celebration. We got that meeting
    tomorrow you know. I am also working on something for your
    grandma.
HACK. What are you working on for Grandma?
TURFIE. I have been watching too many action movies, and yester-
    day, instead of just avoiding a fight, I used violence.

HACK. Beating up a gang member doesn't exactly make you a violent person.

TURFIE. It was the whole gang. I acted like Billy Jack and karate-kicked them. Just once. I did then avoid the second gang. Your grandma is teaching me to turn the other cheek. Malcolm X said before he was assassinated, don't make blanket indictments against whole groups.

HACK. It's not easy to always turn the other cheek, especially when you are seven feet and can do the things you can do.

TURFIE. Do you turn the other cheek?

HACK. Yep, even though it's not always easy. There's a lot of mean people, but my confidence comes and goes, so I don't know if I'm really turning the other cheek or turning chicken. What if you came face to face with this Hoedag that people are claiming to see?

TURFIE. I don't want to hurt it. That just happens to be the thing I want to work on for your grandma. Don't tell anybody.

HACK. What would I say? What does the Hoedag have to do with Grandma?

TURFIE. It's more about turning the other cheek. Race you back to the house silent movie style!

Turfie starts walking back to the house taking small, quick steps keeping his legs and arms like the people in silent movies.

HACK. *(laughing)* Grandma's right, you have been watching too many movies.

Hack attempts to walk the very same way.

DISSOLVE TO

AERIAL SHOT overlooking the lake and the nearby campground area.

CUT TO

Winnie and her camera crew in a wooded area filming an episode of Winnie's Cryptid Crusade.

WINNIE. *(To the camera walking slowly obvious a little frightful)* Now folks from the recent eyewitnesses' accounts, this Hoedag is rather large. And not all accounts are from the lake. There is one where the Hoedag was just offshore. So we may get lucky. I do foresee one problem. All our other nighttime investigations have been done in spots that are a lot more remote. Tonight, we can hear and see activity at the nearby campgrounds. *Winnie's Cryptid Crusade* is all about overcoming obstacles. Here's another.

Winnie calls for the cameramen to stop filming as she walks right into a news crew coming from the other direction.

NEWSWOMAN. We are here with none other than Winnie Washington as she searches for the Hoedag. Winnie, have you encountered the Hoedag?
WINNIE. You know I am not accustomed to conducting interviews in the middle of filming my show. Brandi!

CUT TO

Brandi coming out from behind the cameras.

BRANDI. Let's get your camera and lights off. It's disrupting our serious investigation. This isn't a snipe hunt.
NEWSWOMAN. What's a snipe hunt?
BRANDI. You're joking.
NEWSCAMERAMAN. I know what a snipe hunt is.
BRANDI. Here's your chance of a lifetime. Go show her.

CUT TO

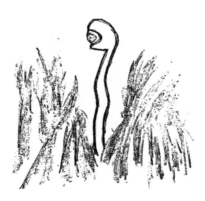

The Hoedag's red eyeball at the end of its tail several yards behind Winnie's crew. It is slowly rising above the brush like a periscope.

CUT TO

SERIES OF SHOTS of Ted's youth church group enjoying their camp out. S'mores, hot dogs, and marshmallows being roasted and eaten. Ted, Reggie, Jay, Amy, and Leslie are standing off to one side.

TED. *(To Reggie)* I appreciate your chaperoning tonight.

REGGIE. My pleasure. Besides, it's the least I can do since you're helping me the next two days.

TED. I am, aren't I? And, Jay, are you ready for your fireside testimony coming up here soon?

JAY. I hope you're not disappointed. You know I'll be unorthodox.

LESLIE. You unorthodox? Imagine that. *(Then to Amy)* Say, Amy, have you met the illustrious Winnie Washington yet?

AMY. No, I haven't. There's got to be a story there by the way you asked.

TED. She greeted Leslie with a zinger.

AMY. Oops, that was a mistake.

LESLIE. You know it.

TED. She's around here somewhere filming an episode of her show.

REGGIE. Looking for the Hoedag.

JAY. That Hoedag isn't going to disrupt your camp outing like the Ditchmen did?

TED. No way. We were lucky though no one got their head smashed by that rowboat.

LESLIE. Where's Turfie?

AMY. He's at the lab doing some last-minute things for his big meeting tomorrow and his Safe Fourth of July Celebration.

REGGIE. Not sure what that could be. We are all ready to go.

Ted, with his guitar, instructs everyone to gather around the fire.

CUT TO

Turfie inside Amy's lab standing in the middle of the conference room its back to the camera. It is staring at a big dry-erase board listing all the unique events for the Safe Fourth of July Celebration. OFF SCREEN "Draggin' the Line" by Tommy James begins to play. Some of the events listed include dodgeball football, kickball golf, water balloons, alley-oop cornhole, dunk the principal, coach's fishpond, two-person whiffie ball tourney, and Freddy Foil volleyball. OFF SCREEN the song "Draggin' the Line" by Tommy James continues as Turfie slowly drags itself away from the conference table toward an elevator.

CUT TO

LONGSHOT of SCRUBS's black Lincoln Town Car parked across the street of Amy's lab.

CUT TO

POV SHOT from the car toward Amy's lab.

SCRUBS AGENT 1. *Do you want us to go in?*

There is no response.

SCRUBS AGENT 1. *I take it that's a no.*

CUT TO

The elevator doors open after descending to the basement lab area. Turfie then dances his way to morgue-like area where he pulls out a big drawer and lifts out a big tub labeled "Dirt Cake remains." Turfie sets it on a counter and retrieves another tub. This tub is labeled "Dirt Cake gummy appendages." Turfie then places the gigantic inflatable water bottle and Stevie's motorcycle helmet also on the counter. Finally, Turfie walks over to a big wooden sliding barn door and opens it. Behind the door is a makeshift temporary dirt wall. Turfie carefully examines it, then backs up to get a running start. After pumping itself up with a couple claps and stomp, Turfie runs and dives shoulder-first into it like a fullback over-the-goal line. Turfie immediately gets up and glances at the tunnel to the bunker under the cemetery caddy corner across the street. It turns on the lights and focuses right on a tub that reads "Ditchmen Positive Dirt." OFF SCREEN the song ends. Turfie then slowly makes his way to the lab. POV SHOT of the cables, empty receptables all leading to the control board. Everything science-related surprisingly looks still intact.

CUT TO

Winnie once again recording an episode of her show in a wooded area near the campgrounds.

WINNIE. Tonight's investigation has already been compromised once so far. As we get nearer to the campgrounds, I feel it is happening again. We can't distinguish between the sounds from the campgrounds and anything that might possibly be in the woods. Let's stop filming. (pause) Brandi.

Brandi makes her way through the crew up to Winnie.

BRANDI. Yes, Winnie, what's up?
WINNIE. (Looking through the woods toward Ted Horn's camp outing) Isn't that the mayor and a bunch of youths around a campfire?
BRANDI. I believe so. Do you want to say hi? I think we are done here.
WINNIE. Yes, but let's wait. It looks like they are getting ready to pray or something.

CUT TO

Ted with everyone now settled around the campfire. He says a quick prayer as they begin their time of worship together. As Ted speaks with his head bowed, Jay signals everyone to put on their yellow mini construction helmets on. It is the kind that is used at kid's birthday parties. He finishes and lifts his head to see the prank that has been pulled on him and to hear the laughter.

TED. Very funny. I guess you will all be safe if another rowboat flies over us. Just for that, Jay, you get no introduction. Here's Jay with his testimony.

JAY. Okay, we're even. Since I didn't get an introduction, you didn't get to hear Ted say all these positive things about me. Well, my message tonight is being positive is a process, and it's a process that you can't do alone.

The youth will laugh when Jay says something funny, and they will then get serious when Jay gets serious.

JAY. I made a lot of poor choices when I was young. I even got pad-dled at school. So me talking about some of my regrets will hopefully help you have less regrets of your own.

HACK. Did it hurt?

JAY. Yes, it hurt so much that I went right to the drinking fountain and sat in it. Then I got paddled two more times for doing that. I was so annoying. I was always doing things like singing a not very nice version of *The Brady Bunch* theme song.

YOUTH. Who's the Brady Bunch?

JAY. Never mind, I am so old. When I was young, I was a quitter. My very first year of playing Little League youth baseball, they had a candy sale fundraiser. Whoever sold the most candy boxes would win a brand-new Schwinn Stingray bicycle. I was bound and determined to win. I went up to my very first house and knocked on the door. A very pretty high school girl answered it. Now when growing up, I had some trouble articulating my *L*s, especially when I got nervous. So I ended up asking, "Do you want to buy any Wittle Weague candy?" She started to laugh and then said that she didn't know if they wanted to buy any Wittle Weague candy. She then called out her mom asking

46

her if they wanted to buy any Wittle Weague candy. Well, I turned around and immediately went home and never tried to sell another box. I just plain gave up. I didn't do much better when I got a little older. I didn't have a youth pastor like the one you got. The ones I had were only concerned about how many souls they could save, like it was a contest. They treated us like boxes of Wittle Weague candy. At age twenty, I started to battle Crohn's disease; and three years later, as most of you know, I had surgery to remove all of my large intestine and three feet of my small intestine. Ever since, I have worn an ileostomy bag. I had no choice but not to be a quitter. And my mom started to tell me to enjoy the struggle.

TED. That's the beginning of having faith.

JAY. I still had to overcome more things as I started college to become a teacher. My professors suggested to me that I try a different career. All because I farted as I taught, due to having an ileostomy bag. I use that for motivation. And that's what you guys have to do when you face disappointment. Stay positive and use it for motivation. Do you guys have any questions?

CUT TO

MEDIUM SHOT of Winnie and her crew watching from the edge of the woods.

CUT TO

No hands going up.

JAY. No questions for me. Then I got one for you. What are your biggest fears or worries?

YOUTH. I worry about being popular.

JAY. I see. Do you know the number one rule for being popular is?

YOUTH. There are rules for being popular.

JAY. Just one. People who are truly popular do not worry about being popular.

47

Everyone gasps.

TED. That is also the beginning of having faith.
ANOTHER YOUTH. I worry about all the mean kids.
TED. We have talked before. They are being mean because they lack love in their lives.
ANOTHER YOUTH. That doesn't help much.
REGGIE. My dad always told me, and you know who that is, that forgiving someone right after they had been mean to you is the best opportunity to be the most like Jesus. Of course, it is very difficult.

Ted turns toward Jay.

TED. You said that? That's beautiful.
JAY. I had to come up with something. Reggie had a habit of retaliating instead of forgiving.
TED. Remember, faith is believing in something you can't see. I believe it's time for our worship song tonight. With all the reports of a Hoedag, I thought of a song that makes you less fearful. It was once a childhood favorite, but some unsubstantiated rumors about the true meaning of the song sort of ruined it for everyone. Here we go. Join me if you know it.

Ted begins to sing "Puff the Magic Dragon" when some of the kids notice Winnie and her crew. They point and interrupt Ted. Winnie and crew then begin to come completely out of the woods toward the campfire.

CUT TO

WiNNIE. No worries, it's just me and my crew.

Everyone around the campfire seems to take a collective sigh of relief. Suddenly, a loud cackle is heard coming from directly behind Winnie and her crew. Everyone takes off, running for cover or at least out the Hoedag's projected path. OFF SCREEN "The Zoo" by the Scorpions once again begins to play. The Hoedag raises its head and long neck from out of the woods like a cobra and begins to slither its way through a number of campsites. Its front chicken-like legs assist the slithering, while the back chicken-like legs become a collector of anything it can clasp onto, including guy ropes, sleeping bags, and lawn chairs. The Hoedag causing lots of screams and mayhem makes its way back into the lake dragging a good part of the campground with it.

CUT TO

What's left of Ted's campsite as the aftermath begins.

TED. Is everyone all right? Ms. Washington, are you hurt?
WINNIE. I'm fine. Call me Winnie. *(She recognizes Leslie)* Why, Mrs. Greer-Horn, how can you look so nice after all that?
LESLIE. Well, when you've been swept off your feet by hundreds of Ditchmen, you learn how to prepare for anything.
WINNIE. That happened to you?

Leslie's attitude toward Winnie changes for the better.

LESLIE. Call me Leslie. Winnie, this is Amy and Jay Griner.
AMY. This is a pleasure. I love your show.

WINNIE. The pleasure is all mine. I have followed your work for some time. This area has had its share of pioneer women in their respective fields. K. C. Geiger, Dr. Elizabeth Kuffner, Nan Davis.

AMY. Wow, you are well informed.

BRANDI. (From behind) Thank you.

WINNIE. That's Brandi, the person who keeps me informed. I met Turfie earlier today. I have got so many things to ask you two.

REGGIE. Excuse me, I'm her son, Reggie. If you want to spend more time with Amy, you should join us for Turfie's Safe Fourth of July Celebration for the youth.

WINNIE. Sounds like a wonderful event.

REGGIE. We have our final organization meeting tomorrow.

WINNIE. I think we can make it. Can we film it?

REGGIE. Sure, that would be wonderful!

WINNIE. Brandi! *(Pause as Brandi draws near)* We may get an episode out of all this yet.

SERIES OF SHOTS of more of the clean up at the various camp sites taking place.

DISSOLVE TO

SERIES OF SHOTS of the next morning as OFF SCREEN "Do it Again" by Steely Dan begins to play. Included in these shots are an LED video wall downtown or on the theater marquee promoting some of tomorrow's local Fourth of July celebration events. There is "Rockin' on Boaters Beach" featuring Deano and the Bubbas. This event is basically a band on a small boat playing in a shallow area where boaters tend to gather and wade or float around. Another event being promoted is Celina's Traditional Amphicar Launch. These amphibious vehicles have a top speed of seven miles per hour on water and seventy miles per hour on land. They were built in Germany from 1961 to 1968. Of those cars, 3,046 were imported into the United States. There are less than six hundred seaworthy still in existence. Finally, the LED video wall shows Turfie's Safe Fourth Celebration for Youths.

As the song continues, a SERIES OF SHOTS of the campgrounds with all the rebuilt, revamped, restored campsites after last night's Hoedag stampede.

CUT TO

Amy's lab as, one by one, participants in Turfie's final meeting before tomorrow arrive one by one, almost like they are arriving at a Hollywood Premiere. Turfie and Reggie are at the door, welcoming all of them. There's Principal Greg, retired sheriff Al, retired police chief Tim, and their spouses. Clay and Debbie, along with their friends Chloe and Tucker. Next Stevie, Coach, Ted, and Leslie follow. Jay and Amy make their entrance. Finally, Winnie, Brandi, and her film crew arrive at the lab. The song ends.

CUT TO

The young boy and girl from the lemonade stand arrive on their bicycles and wave for Turfie to come over. Turfie obliges them.

TURFIE. What's up? You are coming tomorrow, right?
YOUNG BOY. You bet.
YOUNG GIRL. Sure. We just wanted to warn you that we saw some SCUM men yesterday.

Turfie quickly looks back at the lab's door to make sure no one else heard her.

TURFIE. SCUM? Are you sure?
YOUNG BOY. We're sure, but they're not SCUM any more.
YOUNG GIRL. Right, they are now SCRUBS. They explained the acronym, but I can't remember.
TURFIE. "Acronym," you're so smart. Hmm, SCRUBS? That's not much better. Okay, thanks for telling me. Don't worry, I'll handle them.

YOUNG BOY. Special Corp Recovering Underwater Biological Species. I'm smart too!

TURFIE. Yes, you are!

CUT TO the conference room in the lab. Turfie enters and stands with Reggie near the dry-erase board.

REGGIE. Welcome everyone. We are so blessed to have so many special people volunteering to be part of this very special event. It is sure to make this year's Fourth of July for our youth, one they'll never forget. A special thanks to our new friend, Winnie Washington, and her crew, for making this event part of the Hoedag episode.

WINNIE. Thank you for having us. Remember, it is very important to act naturally. We are just here to prove that Turfie there isn't pseudoscience.

AMY. Amen to that!

Everyone cheers for Amy and Turfie.

WINNIE. Did I forget anything, Brandi?

BRANDI. You just need to remind them to remember who the star is.

WINNIE. Right. Remember, I am the star.

REGGIE. Okay, team, let's review our lineup and duties for tomorrow. First up is Principal Greg, who will oversee the dunk tank. Having the courage to do this after what happened to him the last time he did the dunk tank just may make him our MVP.

PRINCIPAL GREG. If ever see a SCUM agent again, I'm going to bring back my paddle.

TURFIE. You may want to bring your paddle with you tomorrow.

AL. Just let us know if you need to help climbing up onto the dunk tank.

PRINCIPAL GREG. You help me? If I remember correctly, you were the guy back in high school who got stuck in a garage door.

Everyone laughs.

REGGIE. Moving right along, we have Coach running our fishpond. Coach, I haven't touched base with you for a while. Are
you good to go with prizes?

COACH. I am good to go. I have a few of my seniors helping me,
and we are ready to put smiles on the faces these young men
and women at the fishpond!

TURFIE. Love that enthusiasm!

REGGIE. Next up, our recently engaged Clay and Debbie monitor-
ing the water balloon cornhole.

Several repeat the event with confusion and curiosity.

WINNIE. Aren't you the skier who used the Hoedag's hump as a
ski ramp?

CLAY. Not on purpose.

WINNIE. We need to interview you later.

CLAY. No problem.

REGGIE. Clay and Debbie, as you see from everyone's reaction, you
are going to have to be able to thoroughly explain your event.

DEBBIE. I think we can handle that. Our whole relationship has involved water. Why should this be any different?

REGGIE. We had purposely revamped a lot of these events just to get the kids out of their comfort zone.

LESLIE. Speaking as a school counselor, they need to learn to try new things. I think this is wonderful.

REGGIE. Of course, we have an expert at thinking outside the box, my dad, Jay.

They clap for Jay.

JAY. Thank you, but I know being able to think outside the box is a nice way to say you are out there.

They now give Jay a chuckle.

REGGIE. Speaking of being out there, Dad, you are next on my lineup card, and your event is dodgeball football.

JAY. All set to go.

TURFIE. Remember, just supervise, not play.

JAY. I'll try.

AMY. Promise him.

JAY. Okay, I promise.

REGGIE. Moving right along, Chloe and Tucker, you will be in charge of Freddie Foil volleyball.

TUCKER. Yes, Reggie. This is my first-year volunteering. What exactly is Freddie Foil volleyball?

JAY. I can explain. All it is is a giant inflatable beachball that has been wrapped in foil. The kids last year named it Freddie. It is basic volleyball with unlimited hits to get it over the net. It requires a lot of teamwork.

TUCKER. Got it. Sounds fun.

REGGIE. Al and Tim, you'll man the two-ball whiffie ball.

WINNIE. Do you mean Wiffle ball?

REGGIE. Uh-oh.

JAY. We around here have always called it whiffie. We learned this unique two-man style of playing from our beloved native Floyd Keith, who, besides a career as a college football coach, was the executive director of the Black Coaches Association from 2001 to 2013. When he was in college, he spent his summers running the local city recreation. He was such a positive influence on so many of us growing up.

AL. He sure was.

TIM. So much fun.

WINNIE. Okay I got it, whiffie ball.

TURFIE. I asked the same thing last year.

WINNIE. What about me? What's my assignment?

REGGIE. You know, Winnie, we could use you to kickball golf.

WINNIE. Sounds intriguing. Brandi!

BRANDI. Got it.

REGGIE. Ted, you will be our rover like you did last year.

CUT TO

SCRUBS in their park vehicle down the street from the lab, obviously staking out the meeting.

CUT TO

REGGIE. As far as concessions, Stevie has graciously donated enough Pizza in a Helmet for everyone.

Everyone cheers.

STEVIE. Proud to do it. Say, Turfie, are you done with my helmet?

TURFIE. Still need it.

AMY. Why do you need Stevie's helmet?

TURFIE. For that thing I've been working on.

JAY. What are working on?

TURFIE. That thing.

JAY. You didn't tell me that you were working on anything.

WINNIE. You told me that you are working on something.

REGGIE. Moving right along, also donating concessions will be Happy Humpty. They will be donating their signature sandwiches, which they renamed after decades.

TED. They don't call it the Big Guy anymore.

REGGIE. It is now called the Big Dude.

JAY. That's smart. Did you have something to do with that?

REGGIE. They are my newest client.

CLAY. Their sign still says Big Guy.

REGGIE. That will be getting changed soon. You ladies have the beverages covered. That's everything I have. If there aren't any questions, we'll see you tomorrow.

SERIES OF SHOTS of everyone making small talk as they slowly make their way to the exit.

WINNIE. Can we ask you two a couple of questions?
AMY. Sure, no problem. Jay, she wants to ask us a couple of questions.
JAY. Shoot.
WINNIE. Amy, why were at one point naming Ditchmen after rock bands and artists snubbed by the Hall of Fame?
AMY. Just my way of protesting the leaving out of so many great rock bands. Bad Company, Boston, Foghat, Styx, Devo, Steppenwolf, Three Dog Night, War, Ohio Players. I could go on and on. Look who is getting in this year, Willie Nelson. Now I respect the fact that he had fourteen failed albums before he finally made it. But what does he have to do with rock and roll?

Winnie notices Turfie about to go down to the lab.

WINNIE. Turfie, aren't we going to meet?
TURFIE. Can you come back in two hours? I'll be ready then.
WINNIE. Okay, I'll be back.
AMY. What's Turfie doing down there?
JAY. It's probably something connected to the event tomorrow.
WINNIE. Now, Jay, test scores are low across the country, but you reportedly had success with your scores.
JAY. She gets a rock and roll question, and I get test scores.
WINNIE. You had a reputation for being a very innovative teacher, that's why.
JAY. If you put it that way, I can answer that question. Teaching is a performance. You're competing against video games and social media. It is vital to make hard work and learning fun. If you think that's impossible, you are already defeated. Now there are two things to keep in mind. First, state departments of education keep moving the goal post. Once test scores improve, they make it more difficult, most likely to justify their cushy state jobs. The bigger the problem, the bigger slice of the state budget the department of education will get. Secondly, regarding spe-

cial education, we are probably the only country who gives the most help to those who need it the most.

AMY. Jay also emphasizes reading for pleasure compared to worrying about what reading level they're at and always assessing what they just read.

WINNIE. Did you two teach Turfie? It seems so educated.

AMY. We can't take credit for that.

JAY. Turfie may be turf, but he absorbs information like a sponge.

AMY. The only thing that we have been trying to teach it is to turn the other cheek. He's been watching too many movies.

JAY. Lately it tries emulating Clint Eastwood and Billy Jack.

WINNIE. Thanks, guys, this episode is turning out to be one of my favorites. It is creating a whole new framework for our show.

CUT TO

Turfie downstairs in Amy's lab. OFF SCREEN "Evil Ways" by Santana begins to play. It stands over an examination table where its nearly finished project rests. Turfie has just finished spraying Flexseal.

Turfie's project consists of an over six-foot inflatable water bottle laying horizontally. Instead of being filled with air, a third of the bottle is filled with the remains of the Dirt Cake, which Amy had stored away. The Dirt Cake's gummy worm appendages strategically protrude out of the bottom, giving it a squid-like look. The remaining two-thirds of the inflatable water bottle is filled with positive-charged dirt used to create past Ditchmen. This dirt had also been stored away by Amy. Strapped on top of this section are two portable cushioned stadium seats. Outstretched on each side of these seats are four Ditchmen arms. Between these two seats, mounted conveniently, is a fully functional industrial water cannon. At the front, over the cap, looking like a trophy head sculpture, is Stevie's helmet. It is a nice finishing touch to Turfie's water dirt bike. The song pauses.

TURFIE. All it needs is a little jolt, and it will be ready to embark. But how much of a jolt does it need? This is where I need Amy. I don't dare use the main terminal workstation under the cemetery. That could result in too much juice.

Turfie pauses to think.

TURFIE. I got it! This should work.

Turfie picks up the water dirt bike much like he had picked up Amy in the parking garage and starts for the elevator.

TURFIE. Whoa, you are a little more difficult to haul than Amy.

CUT TO

SERIES OF SHOTS of people enjoying the night before the Fourth of July. The song "Evil Ways" by Santana continues. Coach is outside on his patio, preparing to grill out. His grilling area now has a small roof over it. Youth baseball and adult softball games are in progress at the local K. C. Geiger Park. We see the repaired campsites at the campgrounds, where campers are hopefully enjoying a much quieter evening. Clay and Tucker are both parked outside Have a Fit, Stay Fit, waiting for Debbie and Chloe to lock up. Turfie, carrying his project, sneaks out of the lab, looking to quickly run from one shadow area to another so as not to be seen. The song pauses.

CUT TO

Inside the SCRUBS car, which is staking out the lab

SCRUB AGENT 1. What is going on?

CUT TO

The Griner farm where Reggie and Hack are playing catch in the front yard. Jay and Amy are watching them as they swing on the porch swing. Jay starts to sing the last verse of "Glory of Love" by Frank DeVol.

JAY. You've got to win a little, lose a little
Yes, and always have the blues a little
That's the story of, that's the glory of love.

There is a pause for a moment as they cuddle.

JAY. What are you thinking?
AMY. I'm so grateful you and Reggie have had this opportunity to resolve your differences.
JAY. They weren't exactly major differences. He just thought I was too overprotective.
AMY. He needed protection. He didn't have the same start in life as others.
JAY. It was hard walking that tightrope of protecting him from the world and keeping my expectations for him high. You know, not allow him to be a victim even when he had good reason to be.
AMY. It worked. He overcame it, he is successful. He's got a wife joining him here soon. And of course, there's Hack.
JAY. It was so hard to say to him when he was discouraged, "If you can't stand the heat get out of the stove."

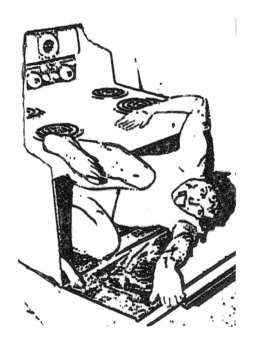

AMY. Yes, he wasn't a quitter, but it's *kitchen* not *stove*.

JAY. What?

AMY. You were a language arts teacher. The idiom is, "If you can't stand the heat get out of the *kitchen*" not *stove*.

JAY. I always mess that one up. How do you get in a stove in the first place, before you even try to get out of one?

Hack and Reggie finish playing catch and come over to the front porch.

CUT TO

Long shot of a couple of fireworks going off in town at different locations.

HACK. Grandma, why are there fireworks in town? It's only July third.

REGGIE. Those are not the main fireworks.

AMY. Those are people having their private fireworks.
JAY. They just couldn't wait until tomorrow.

CUT TO

The lake, where the Hoedag pops his head above the water, noticing the private fireworks in the distance.

CUT TO

Turfie inconspicuously runs up to an electric vehicle charging station and attempts to give a jolt to the water dirt bike that it created.

TURFIE. I knew it, not enough juice.

Turfie then starts heading quickly back to the lab, also inconspicuously. The song "Evil Ways" by Santana resumes.
SERIES OF SHOTS again of Coach grilling on his patio under his new roof built after the night his grill got bombed by a launched corpse.
The softball game and youth baseball game are still underway, now under the lights. An outfielder is shown specifically making a nice running catch. At the youth baseball game, a mother is specifically shown trying to give her son a bottled drink as he stands on the on-deck circle. Embarrassed, he rudely shakes head no and waves her away.
We see the campgrounds as marshmallows and hot dogs are being roasted. One older camper is shown making sure his campsite items are nice and secure and won't be dragged away.
Next Clay and Tucker are shown standing outside their vehicles chatting as they continue to wait on Debbie and Chloe.
Finally, a quick camera shot of Jay and Amy still on the porch swing. The song ends.

CUT TO

SCRUBS still staking out the lab.

CUT TO

Winnie and her crew trying to get someone to answer the door at the lab. It isn't long before Turfie returns to the lab.

TURFIE. Sorry you had to wait for me.

WINNIE. We just got here ourselves. Is this it? Oh my!

TURFIE. I call it a DMDC Water Dirt Bike.

BRANDI. DMDC?

TURFIE. Ditchmen, Dirt Cake. You see the back third is the remains of the Dirt Cake. The front two-thirds, including the arms, are Ditchmen. It should travel through water faster than a Jet Ski. The gummy arms stick out of the bottom and will have the same jet propulsion system as a squid. And I've attached this water cannon pump system so it can be like a tugboat without being deadly. You see, Amy wants me to be less violent.

WINNIE. No more Billy Jack.

TURFIE. You got it. Now I'm still one major step away though.

WINNIE. And what's that.

TURFIE. It needs to have a jolt of electricity to be in working condition. Once it gets that, it should operate on command.

WINNIE. That's fascinating. Are you guys getting all this?

BRANDI. They are.

WINNIE. It's like AI versus Cryptid.

TURFIE. The DMDC Water Dirt Bike might be AI, but I'm AT.

WINNIE. "AT"?

TURFIE. Artificial turf. (chuckles) I've used that a lot in three days.

WINNIE. You are so delightful. Now how do you achieve this final step?

TURFIE. I just tried an EV charging station to no avail. I do have an idea, and with your help, it could work. It will be a little tricky.

WINNIE. What can we do?

TURFIE. I'll tell you what—I'll run and get the megaphone for you. Then if you could go over there across the street and down to that cemetery and press the alarm button if the graves start shaking, I'll hear it.

WINNIE. I'm afraid I'm not following you.

TURFIE. I'm leaving out a whole bunch. You know Amy had an underground lab under that cemetery.

WINNIE. And something backfired back in October.

TURFIE. And I was made because she had only one positive charge cannister under one grave.

WINNIE. But all the other corpses were launched out of their graves.

TURFIE. That had to be a sight. I wouldn't know because it took another jolt of electricity—this time, lightning two days later—to bring me completely to life. Now all the electrical cables are surprisingly still hooked up to the burial vaults and the main terminal down there.

WINNIE. Brandi, this episode is going to hit the jackpot.

BRANDI. Don't say my name, we are filming.

WINNIE. I can't help it. This is so exciting.

TURFIE. Anyways, the lab under the cemetery is still fully functional. Amy doesn't know I know. But I will go under the cemetery from the lab's basement and give DMDC enough of jolt to awaken it.

WINNIE. And the grave's shaking will indicate too much juice.

TURFIE. You got it!

WINNIE. Okay, let's do this!

TURFIE. Places, everyone. Oh, after I get you the megaphone.

Turfie runs inside.

CUT TO

POV SHOT from SCRUBS's stake out vehicle.

SCRUBS AGENT 1. What is going on?

MS. GREEN. I believe it's time we made our move.

SCRUBS AGENT 1. With pleasure, Ms. Green.

Dianne Green, the EPA representative who was part of that task force nearly two years ago with Stan Bando, gets out of the car along with four SCRUBS agents who are still dressed in their aquatic fashion clothes. They start walking toward the cemetery.

CUT TO

WINNIE giving her crew instructions in the cemetery.

WINNIE. I'll say it again—we've hit the jackpot here. If we can get on film a confrontation between the Hoedag and Turfie…
MS. GREEN. You can just forget getting anything else on film.
WINNIE. Who are you?
MS. GREEN. My name is Green. I was stuck here two years ago as part of the task force investigating the Ditchmen. At that time, I represented the Environmental Protection Agency. Now let's just say I have moved up to a more specific role with a lot more authority.
BRANDI. Stan Bando was on that task force. He was behind the creation of the Dirt Cake.
MS. GREEN. Stan Bando is a loser. My missions are always successful.
WINNIE. And what is your mission?
MS. GREEN. Oh, this is an easy one. My mission is to diffuse the situation.
BRANDI. What situation?
MS. GREEN. The Hoedag. And to diffuse the Hoedag, I need you to stop filming.
WINNIE. I have a show to finish.
MS. GREEN. I'll tell you what. I'll let you finish your show if it ends with you eliminating the Hoedag.

Winnie and her crew react with disbelief and refusal.

WINNIE. Why is a former EPA agent—and now I'm guessing still connected to the EPA—asking for the extinction of a newly discovered species?

MS. GREEN. I don't have to answer that question, but I am going to because I think you are smart enough to see things my way. From the 1880s to the 1910s there were more than 150 oil wells in and around Grand Lake St. Marys. Then a potentially bigger oil field was discovered in Texas. Well, these greedy individuals packed it up here prematurely. My mission specifically is to keep anyone from rediscovering the oil at all costs. That Hoedag is attracting too much attention to the lake. Finding that oil isn't going to help the climate. So will you help me, or will I need to have SCRUBS do it for you?

WINNIE. SCRUBS?

MS. GREEN. Special Corp Recovering Underwater Biological Species. In this case, it happens to be eliminating as opposed to recovering. Take a moment to soak all this in.

CUT TO

Turfie is now under the cemetery in Amy's lab. It is finishing hooking up DMDC to the main terminal. Turfie then gives DMDC a little jolt, and nothing happens. Turfie shakes head in disgust and then looks up. It calls Winnie's name, but no way is she going to hear Turfie. Turfie then decides to stand on the main terminal and attempts to stick its head through the dirt roof of the lab in order to contact Winnie and her crew. Turfie's head pokes through and begins to witness everything, including the tail end of what Ms. Green just explained.

CUT TO

Winnie responding to Dianne Green's ultimatum.

WINNIE. Ms. Green, how do you choose between being a climate activist over protecting a new species? Shouldn't you be doing both?

MS. GREEN. Sacrifices must be made. We will provide you with shark spear guns, so it can be done quietly. People will accept you having a mishap with a cryptid that you love as opposed to the government.

WINNIE. "Sacrifices must be made." That usually means this is about money!

CUT TO

Turfie losing its balance and falling back on the main terminal, resulting in accidently turning on the electrical charges full blast. The DMDC Water Dirt Bike starts shaking profusely. Every vault to every grave start tremoring as well.

TURFIE. Oh no, I didn't want to do that!

CUT TO

SERIES OF SHOTS as the song "My City Was Gone" by the Pretenders begins to play. Dianne Green and SCRUBS agents look around terrified and take off running as corpses and the other contents of the coffins start blasting off. Winnie and her crew also look around horrified before they take off, running while pushing the PA speaker alarm button.

WINNIE. Brandi!
BRANDI. You didn't give her an answer!
WINNIE. She didn't deserve one!

CUT TO

LONG SHOT of the cemetery as the fireworks of cadavers continues.

CUT TO

Amy and Jay's porch swinging being interrupted by Hack and Reggie pointing toward town at the unusual fireworks.

HACK. What kind of fireworks are those?

Amy stands and moves to the end of the porch.

AMY. Jay! It can't be happening again. It is!
JAY. Does this have anything to do with Turfie's project?
AMY. Nobody knows—not even Turfie—that I had been in there working again until I had you block the entrance.
JAY. So.
AMY. I connected cables and receptacles to the pet cemetery next to it.
JAY. You mean this could be a bigger launch?
AMY. And scarier. Pets! We've got to get to town!

They all dash to Jay's vehicle as Hack asks a dozen questions.

CUT TO

The softball game as a hitter hits what an outfielder thought was a flyball. He tracks the ball back, reaches out, and catches a skull. His reaction is one of shock and fear.

CUT TO

   The youth baseball game as carcasses start landing on the field.

CUT TO

   The player who was rude earlier to his mom now running to her like a frightened toddler.

CUT TO

   A baseball landing near one softball player. He runs and picks it up.

SOFTBALL PLAYER. Wow! Look, everybody, a Pete Rose autographed baseball!

   Nobody is interested, they are all running for cover.

CUT TO

   Coach, with no potato chips around, looking for his spatula.

COACH. I always lose my dang spatula.

Coach starts to walk inside to get a spatula when a stiff crashes into the roof covering his grill. Coach is in disbelief that it happened again.

CUT TO

The parking lot where Clay and Jay are watching the pandemonium. They are joined by a frightened Debbie and Chloe.

DEBBIE. Not again.
CLAY. Yes again. We've got to get to the lab.

CUT TO

The lemonade stand siblings coming out the front door of their house.

YOUNG BOY. I'm confused. Is it the Fourth of July, or Trick or Treat again?
YOUNG GIRL. Pretty sure it's the Fourth of July tomorrow.

CUT TO

The middle of Grand Lake St. Marys as a few pets launched from the pet cemetery land near the Hoedag. It gives a Hoedag growl and submerges.

CUT TO

SERIES OF SHOTS at the campgrounds as pet carcasses land near and around campers. One young camper looks up and watches a dog's head plummeting straight for the wiener that he was roasting. Others run, dropping the marshmallows that they were about to enjoy. The camper who had secured his campsite from another attack from the ground watches helplessly as a couple of pet remains descend and land on his camper, lodging themselves partially through the roof. Screams from inside immediately proceed. The song ends.

CUT TO

SERIES OF SHOTS of first responders coming and going everywhere.

CUT TO

One officer sees movement in the dark near the lab and cemetery. He doesn't know it, but it is Turfie.

OFFICER. Hey, you over there, stop!

The officer runs over to where he saw movement and looks around.

CUT TO

The officer's feet, which are standing on Turfie pretending to be the ground. The officer eventually moves off him and back to the street. Turfie then gets up and scampers into the darkness.

DISSOLVE TO

SERIES OF SHOTS of emergency crews this Fourth of July morning still cleaning up from the cemetery fireworks that took place on the third of July. Some media crews are now there.

CUT TO

LONG SHOT of the Griner Farm.

CUT TO

Inside the Griner Farm, as breakfast is being eaten to begin this busy day. Everyone is eating around the table except Turfie, who is just standing nearby with his head down.

TURFIE. I am so, so sorry!

AMY. You've just got to let it go, Turfie. You have a big day ahead of you. Besides, it's my fault, I shouldn't have gone back in there, rigged everything back up to make it fully operational. Jay, you should have stopped me!

JAY. I did stop you. I blocked the entrance.

HACK. Turfie made a cool, wet dirt bike.

AMY. How did you know what to do with those remains?

TURFIE. I've observed the best.

JAY. Quit observing me.

HACK. Not you, Grandma.

REGGIE. You should tell them what you told me about what you heard.

AMY. What did you hear?

TURFIE. Winnie's crew was in the cemetery with the megaphone. They were going to push the alarm if the graves started to shake. You see, I was only going to give it just a little jolt of electricity. But I heard strange voices, so I stood on the terminal and poked my head up through the ground. There was this woman named Green threatening Winnie to kill the Hoedag.

JAY. Kill the Hoedag?

AMY. That had to be Dianne Green, EPA's representative on the task force. Why on earth would she want Winnie to kill the Hoedag?

TURFIE. You're close. Not on earth, but because of what is below earth.

AMY. I'm not following. What do you mean "below earth"?

TURFIE. Oil. Evidently there's still a lot of oil under the lake, and Ms. Green wants nobody to know about that. She wants Winnie to do it so it would be less controversial, but she'll have SCRUBS do it if she doesn't.

JAY. SCRUBS?

TURFIE. That's SCUM's new acronym. Special Corp Recovering Underwater Species.

JAY. I can't believe they're back. Green should be protecting both the climate and the wildlife. Not choosing one over the other.

AMY. Unless there's money involved.

TURFIE. It sounded like Winnie wanted nothing to do with it. That's when I lost my balance and fell back onto the terminal accidentally turning everything on full power.

REGGIE. I know this is very important stuff, but we have an event put on today.

AMY. You're right. That should be our focus.

HACK. When can I ride the DMDC?

JAY. DMDC?

TURFIE. Ditchmen Dirt Cake Wet Dirt Bike.

AMY. You weren't successful at making it fully operational, were you?

TURFIE. Yep, it works.

Everyone at the table just take a long curious look at each other.

CUT TO

AERIAL SHOT from a drone on the west bank of the lake near downtown Celina where the Amphicars are about to be put into the

73

water. There is a lot of pomp and circumstance involved with this event, and it draws quite a crowd. There is even an emcee giving the crowd a play by play, and it happens to be Mr. Macamee. The skinny elderly gentleman is wearing his usual white-collar shirt, plaid shorts, black dress shoes, and black dress socks.

MR. MACAMEE. First, let me just say I feel very honored to be asked to emcee the Amphicar Put in the Water Event even though I am from the town across the lake, St. Marys.

CUT TO

The crowd booing.

CUT TO

MR. MACAMEE. My mistake for reminding you of that. Now I know the traditional "Put in the Lake" we all know is your Celina Lake Festival, I think it fitting that we also include this as part of your Fourth of July Celebration. As most of you know, 3,878 of these Amphicars were built in Germany from 1961 to 1968. Of those cars, 3,046 were imported and only 600 exist today. The Amphicar has a top speed of seven miles per hour on the water, and seventy miles per hour on land. Enough of the background information. Ladies and gentlemen, start your engines!

CUT TO

The crowd cheering as the vehicles begin to drive into the water.

CUT TO

The AERIAL VIEW from a drone of the spectacular sight. Suddenly the view is obstructed by the mouth of the Hoedag launching from the water and consuming the drone right out of the sky like a dog catching a frisbee. It then falls back into the water, creating a monumental splash.

CUT TO

SERIES OF SHOTS of the crowd displaying a helpless frenzy and drivers doing their best to quickly turn around and drive out of the water.

CUT TO

Mr. Macamee pleading with the drivers to be faster.

MR. MACAMEE. Come on faster, faster. You gotta be fast and furious not slow and tedious.

CUT TO

The East Bank of Grand Lake St. Marys where Turfie's Safe Fourth of July Celebration Event is just getting underway.

SERIES OF SHOTS of the various stations and concessions. Principal Greg sternly pointing out that he had requested a dunk tank with a protective screen, so before he climbs up on to the tank, he over-emphasizes that the balls are to be thrown at the appropriate small round target. Once he gets in place, the throwing begins with no one coming close and Principal Greg enjoying their lack of accuracy.

PRINCIPAL GREG. Maybe you need to throw a bigger ball. You know, I once pitched a baseball game with a bowling ball. Try that. It was quite effective, especially my bean ball.

CUT TO

Coach, with the help of a couple of his football players, managing the fish pond station. The fish pond has cleverly been placed so that Coach is between the barrier and the lake. This gives the children the appearance that they are fishing right out of the lake. It's not long before everyone notices that the prize that Coach and his players are putting in the pouch on the end of the fishing line is small bags of potato chips.

CUT TO

The confused look of several of the youths as they reach into the pouch and pull out the small bag of potato chips.

CUT TO

Clay and Debbie demonstrating how to play water balloon cornhole.

CLAY. Your partner will toss a water balloon toward the hole on the cornhole board. You are allowed to try and guide it into the hole, sort of like an alley-oop in basketball. Go ahead, Debbie, toss one.

Debbie goes ahead and tosses a water balloon, and Clay guides it into the hole. The water balloon bursts, however, giving Clay a quick shower. Everyone erupts in laughter.

CUT TO

Jay and Amy explaining the rules for dodgeball football.

JAY. Dodgeball football is basically the sport ultimate frisbee, but with a dodgeball instead of a frisbee. Now one team will wear a white wristband on your right hand, so you can tell the two teams apart. Your goal is to have a teammate catch the dodgeball in your end zone. You cannot run with the dodgeball. You throw it to a teammate. If the dodgeball touches the ground, it no longer belongs to the team that touched it last. You are allowed to intercept. Finally, you must stay ten yards away from whoever holds the dodgeball. Let's give it a try.

SERIES OF SHOTS of dodgeball football being played.

CUT TO

SERIES OF SHOTS of Freddie Foil Volleyball already in progress.

CHLOE. That's good! Remember, you have an unlimited number of hits on Freddie! All he is is a giant beach ball wrapped up in foil!

The teams start chanting "Freddie, Freddie."

CUT TO

Retired sheriff Al and retired police chief Tim organizing the two-man whiffie ball tournament. Tim is holding a poster with the brackets as Al explains the rules.

AL. The brackets are set. Now we'll have two games going on at once. We'll use the Floyd Keith rules from the old summer city recreation days. This means there are five innings, one out per half inning. One player pitches, while the other plays left and center field. Right field is an automatic out. Sorry, left-handed batters, it is totally unfair. But you get to learn a very valuable lesson, and that is life is unfair. Getting back to the rules, there must always be a batter able to bat. That means there is always a force out at home if there is a runner on base. Also, batters may wait for a good pitch.

CUT TO

Winnie gathering the kids at her station to her.

WINNIE. Gather up, everybody, gather up. Now do I have everybody's attention? Good. Brandi here will now explain how we'll play kickball golf.
BRANDI. Okay, we have four kickballs, so we'll have four of you go at a time. The objective is to kick the kickball into this weighted fitness hula hoop laying on the ground in the least number of attempts.

CUT TO

Leslie, with the help of Al and Tim's spouses, organizing the concession areas.

LESLIE. Now we'll have the Pizzas in Helmets over here on these picnic tables and the Happy Humpty's Big Dude hamburgers over on these tables. Drinks will be over at the end.

CUT TO

A Happy Humpty van pulling up followed by two Helmet Pizza Vans.

CUT TO

Stevie getting out of one. He is greeted by Turfie.

TURFIE. Is it in the other van?

Stevie gives Turfie the thumbs-up.

CUT TO

Ted walking over to Reggie.

TED. Where would you like me?
REGGIE. Well, originally, I had you down as a rover, but after last
    night, you better also keep an eye out for the media. If they find
    out Amy is here, they'll mob her. Maybe Winnie too.
TED. Roger that.
REGGIE. You probably should keep an eye out for Ms. Green and
    her SCRUBS. You do know why they were here.
TED. I heard, keeping possible oil fields a secret at the cost of the
    Hoedag. That's just plain wrong.
REGGIE. It's all about money.

CUT TO

*SERIES OF SHOTS of every station now in full progress as the
song "Dusic" by Brick begins to play. Principal Greg not getting dunked.
Coach not so thrilling kids as they catch small bags of potato chips at the
fishpond. Other youth guiding water balloons into the cornhole target
only to have them burst. A couple of touchdowns at dodgeball football.
Exciting close diving force outs at home during the two-man whiffle ball
tournament. Freddie Foil going back and forth over the net. Finally,
kickball golf successful attempts to get the ball in the circle created by the
weighted fitness hoop. The song ends.*

CUT TO

    The Boaters Beach area where the local cover band Deano and the Bubbas are carefully placed on a pontoon just offshore. Deano announces enjoying this Fourth of July before beginning to play the next song, "Just Another Night" by Ian Hunter of the band Mott the Hoople. The band is scattered on all sides by all kinds of boats. Some of the people stay on their boats; others stand in the shallow waters. Several lay on flotation devices.

DEANO. *(Singing the chorus)* Just another night!
CROWD. Just another night!
DEANO. Just another night on the other side of life!

CUT TO

    The Hoedag's hump approaching the concert on the lake as this back-and-forth chorus is repeated. And as before, it looks like a massive shark fin going in reverse or a shark doing the moon walk.

    The Hoedag reaches the boaters. The water is too shallow for the hump to remain submerged, and it starts it clobber boat after boat. The blunt thump easily knocks boaters into the water. Oddly enough, those wading and in floaties make a mad dash for their boats to get out of the water, only to be bumped right back in. Eventually the Hoedag's hump slams into the band's boat, sending them into the lake with their audience.

CUT TO

    Leslie, Stevie, and the rest of the concession helpers putting the finishing touches on the food and drink area. After some discussion, Leslie grabs the megaphone and pushes the alarm button.

LESLIE. *(Into the megaphone)* Come and get it!

    Everyone at every station stops what they're doing and starts running toward Leslie.

LESLIE. *(To her volunteers nearby)* How do you stop a stampede?
STEVIE. *{pointing behind her}* That's how!

CUT TO

    The Hoedag rising out of the water and then coming on shore.

CUT TO

    Leslie turning around and screaming into the megaphone.

CUT TO

The stampede of children coming to a complete stop.

CUT TO

The Hoedag slithering toward the concession area.

SERIES OF SHOTS *of the Hoedag efficiently using his tail with the eye to start grabbing and slinging the Big Dude double-decker cheeseburgers. The very first burger hurled hits Principal Greg on the dunk tank, knocking him into the water for the very first time today. Other burgers start hitting the fleeing youths on the backs of their heads as they retreat. A couple burgers whack the cornhole players and fall in the hole. The volunteers are also targeted. Stevie's van takes a couple brutal pelts. The Pizzas in Helmets are next. They are flipped off the table by the tail, landing like grenades among the crowd. Some kids make a counterattack by volleying Freddie Foil right at it. The Hoedag just raises head up high and smashes Freddie with the base of his jaw. Everyone at this event is horrified. Suddenly, the Hoedag stops when he hears numerous air horns coming from the Jet Skis idling behind him right offshore.*

CUT TO

Three members of SCRUBS on three Jet Skis. They are pointing shark spear guns right at the Hoedag. Ms. Green is on a nearby boat with a fourth member of SCRUBS. She is using her megaphone to bark out some orders.

MS. GREEN. Everyone, just stand back. My men have it in their
    sights. We wouldn't want any innocent bystanders to get hurt.
WINNIE. Have them put those spear guns down!
MS. GREEN. You had your chance.
AMY. Stop it right now!

CUT TO

Turfie making his way to the van containing the DMDC Water Dirt Bike. He begins to open the back as Ms. Green gives a firing countdown.

CUT TO

MS. GREEN. Ready, aim, fire!

CUT TO

The SCRUBS fire their shark spear guns right at the Hoedag, only to be intercepted by Turfie, who takes all three spears right into his turf-

field body. The spears have no negative effect on Turfie. The Hoedag immediately roars like a fire-breathing dragon minus the fire and then begins its countercharge. Turfie, still with the spears sticking through its midsection, manages to climb upon the back of the Hoedag. This causes Hoedag to abort its counterattack and concentrate on displacing Turfie. In and out of the water surface like a bronco, the Hoedag goes.

CUT TO

SCRUBS on their Jet Skis make their adjustments and begin their pursuit of the Hoedag, and so does as Ms. Green in her boat.

CUT TO

Jay, Amy, and Winnie rallying everyone after the bombardment that they just went through.

WINNIE. Jay, Amy, you got to do something!
JAY. We got to do something, Amy, but what?
HACK. Grandpa, DMDC, the water dirt bike, it's right over there.
REGGIE. Come on, Hack, let's get it!

They quickly go, get the DMDC, and bring it to the shore, where Jay climbs on it.

REGGIE. *(After trying to get on the back seat)* There's just not enough
    room with that water cannon there. I'm just too big.
HACK. *(Climbing on quickly)* Not me.
REGGIE. Hack, get off! It's too dangerous.
JAY. No time to argue. How do you start this thing?
AMY. Just say go!
REGGIE. Make sure your life jackets are on good!

Suddenly the Ditchmen arms act like seatbelts and grasp on tightly to Jay and Hack. The gummy arms sticking out the back to begin to jet-propel, and off the wet dirt bike goes. The song "Beatin' the Odds" by Molly Hatchet begins to play. It goes in and out according to what is happening at the time.

CUT TO

    Amy, Winnie, and everyone else at the event.

WINNIE. That was the bravest thing I ever witnessed, and I've witnessed a lot of brave things.
AMY. By whom?
WINNIE. All three.

CUT TO

    Winnie's film crew arriving on the scene.

WINNIE. Brandi, why did I give my film crew the day off?
BRANDI. I don't know. It was pretty human of you.
AMY. All I can see is the Hoedag and Turfie occasionally flying out of the water.
TED. Leaps of faith, Amy, leaps of faith.
WINNIE. You are so right.

CUT TO

    A large group of kids consoling the smashed Freddie Foil.

CUT TO

    Jay and his grandson, Hack, catching up to Ms. Green's boat.

JAY. Okay Hack, are you ready to test out that water cannon?
HACK. You bet.
JAY. Aim for that boat.

Hack aims the water cannon and starts blasting at Ms. Green's boat. It is powerful enough to knock Ms. Green down. The SCRUBS driver turns to help Ms. Green, and Hack blasts him right out of the boat causing it to stop running.

Jay yells as he draws near to one of the SCRUBS Jet Skiers. Hack, gaining confidence with his aim, blasts the SCRUBS guy right off his Jet Ski. Hack then repeats this as they get close to the next SCRUBS Jet Skiers. The celebration continues, and they soon dismount the final SCRUBS off his Jet Ski.

They now try to zoom on the Hoedag.

CUT TO

Some boys and girls on a banana boat tube. They are yelling a request to be blasted by the water cannon, so Hack obliges.

CUT TO

The Hoedag still breaching like a dolphin, attempting to have Turfie lose its grip.

CUT TO

The boaters beach concert finally resuming after Deano and the Bubbas got some instruments to replace their wet, damaged ones.

CUT TO

The Hoedag leaping a little higher and crashing back down in the water, creating a small tsunami that sends the boaters and band back into the water.

CUT TO

The west bank as Mr. Macamee announcing the second attempt of the Amphicar put into the water event. He notices the Hoedag approaching.

MR. MACAMEE. Oh no, not again! Abort, abort! And the Hoedag is not alone this time.

CUT TO

SERIES OF SHOTS of the Amphicars reversing course and returning to the docks at their maximum seven miles per hour.

CUT TO

The Hoedag reversing its course. As soon as it does, it notices Jay and Hack closing in. The Hoedag launches another high breach almost entirely perpendicular to the surface, creating a splash that overturns Jay, Hack, and the DMDC Wet Dirt Bike.

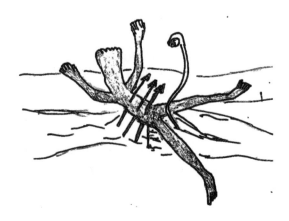

CUT TO

The Hoedag heading for a cavity that produced natural gas back in the 1880. There is a crack in the lake bottom that leads to this cavity. The Hoedag, with just enough effort, manages to squirm into the crack. Turfie is unable to get through the crack due to the three spears still in it. Turfie, no longer holding on, quickly starts looking for large rocks to cover the crack.

CUT TO

The SCRUBS with Ms. Green arriving in this area. One SCRUBS agent is back on a Jet Ski.

CUT TO

Jay exploding out of the water and yanking the SCRUBS agent right off the Jet Ski and propelling himself on it.

JAY. *(Making a proclamation to Ms. Green and SCRUBS)* The Hoedag is safe, and the oil secret is no longer a secret. You have failed! Have a nice life!

Jay goes and picks up Hack floating nearby, and they start heading back to the east bank. Due to the noise of the Jet Ski, they must talk loud.

HACK. What about Turfie and DMDC?

JAY. They'll be fine.

HACK. How can you be sure?

JAY. What's Ted been trying to teach you?

HACK. "Don't be afraid to take leaps of faith," but what does that mean exactly?

JAY. Faith is believing in something you can't see.

HACK. You know that seems a lot like your mantra, "Enjoy the struggle."

JAY. You know, Hack, you make me one proud grandpa! Let's get back.

CUT TO

Turfie underwater finishing covering the crack in the natural gas cavity with many rocks. Because Turfie doesn't need oxygen, it can take its time and make its way over to where DMDC is lying on the lake's floor. Turfie pulls out the three spears and then begins to raise the wet dirt bike to the surface.

CUT TO

The east bank as Amy, using binoculars, tries to spot Jay, Hack, and Turfie.

AMY. I see Jay and Hack. They are on a Jet Ski though, not DMDC.

Everyone nearby cheers.

CUT TO

Jay and Hack arriving at the shore. After Amy's hug, Winnie is next to get his attention.

WINNIE. Did the Hoedag make it? And where's Turfie?

JAY. I'm not positive, but they must have. Green and her SCRUBS took off with their tails between their legs.

AMY. I don't think anything can hurt Turfie. What about DMDC?

JAY. We capsized, and it sank.

AMY. Hmm, not sure how that could happen.

JAY. Reggie, you got a fine son there.

REGGIE. I know.

WINNIE. Amy, your binoculars, there's something out there!

AMY. It's Turfie! On DMDC!

HACK. DMDC is working?

AMY. Not exactly, Turfie is using his legs as paddles.

WINNIE. Brandi, have them start filming.

CUT TO

Turfie on DMDC using his long flat legs as the perfect paddles.

CUT TO

Winnie very enthusiastically taking charge.

WINNIE. Brandi! In fact, not just Brandi, but everybody! I got an idea for the perfect welcome back. Turfie's a huge fan of the movie *Billy Jack*, so let's recreate the final scene. Here's what we need to do.

CUT TO

POV SHOT from the shore of Turfie getting closer and closer. Amy is the first to greet Turfie with a hug. Reggie, Hack, and Stevie help carry DMDC out of the water and toward Stevie's van. Turfie stops them momentarily to take the helmet off DMDC, revealing just the bottle top filled with dirt. Turfie hands the helmet back to Stevie. Winnie then grabs Turfie by the hand.

WINNIE. You have had a rough day. You've done a lot of good today. Jay's waiting to take you home in his truck.

Turfie looks up and sees everyone involved with his Safe Fourth of July Celebration sitting down and forming two rows with an opening in the middle for Turfie to walk through.

TURFIE. Hey, this is just like in *Billy Jack*.
WINNIE. Not exactly like, but very similar.

The song "One Tin Soldier" by Original Caste begins to play. Turfie begins walking through the welcoming gauntlet. As it reaches each person, they stand up and give Turfie either a low or high five. The more it goes through it, the more enthusiastic it becomes. Turfie eventually reaches Jay's truck at the end and climbs into its bed. Amy arrives and gets into the passenger seat with Jay, the driver.

JAY. Home, dear? I need to rest.
AMY. You can get started installing our new bidet.
JAY. No time for that. We've got to watch the Fourth of July fireworks.

Reggie and Hack reach the truck and climb onto its bed. From Billy Jack *to* Wizard of Oz, *Jay now drives away like Dorothy leaving Munchkinland down the Yellow Brick Road. The children follow, waving like the Munchkins.*

OFF SCREEN the song "Soul Deep" covered by The Box Tops begins to play. Closing credits are shown.

ABOUT THE AUTHOR

In 1984, Joe Ginter had his colon removed due to Crohn's disease, along with three feet of his small intestine and his rectum. On welfare for just a month and facing the rest of his life wearing an ostomy bag, using the motto inspired by his mom "Enjoy the struggle," he rebounded to become a fifth- and sixth-grade teacher for thirty-four years. He accomplished this despite some of his college professors suggesting he choose a different career due to the farting noises originating from his ostomy. Before his teaching career, he dabbled in stand-up comedy and writing.

With the lack of clean comedy in the market, Joe decided to write *Ditchmen, Ditchmen 2*, and *Ditchmen 3* using his classes as test audiences and advisors. Ditchmen were imaginary creatures that he sketched when he was four years old as his family would drive down country roads to visit his grandparents.

Printed in the USA
CPSIA information can be obtained
at www.ICGtesting.com
LVHW021604010424
776102LV00009B/226